Go Away!

and

.et's Make a Rocket

'Go Away!' and 'Let's Make a Rocket'
An original concept by Elizabeth Dale
© Elizabeth Dale

Illustrated by Gina Lorena Maldonado

Published by MAVERICK ARTS PUBLISHING LTD

Studio 3A, City Business Centre, 6 Brighton Road,

Horsham, West Sussex, RH13 5BB

© Maverick Arts Publishing Limited May 2018

+44 (0)1403 256941

A CIP catalogue record for this book is available at the British Library.

ISBN 978-1-84886-350-7

www.maverickbooks.co.uk

This book is rated as: Red Band (Guided Reading)
This story is decodable at Letters and Sounds Phase 2.

Go Away!

and

Let's Make a Rocket

By **Elizabeth Dale**

Illustrated by **Gina Lorena Maldonado**

The Letter O

Trace the lower and upper case letter with a finger. Sound out the letter.

Around

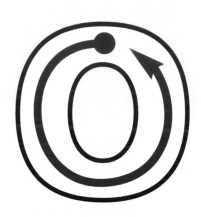

Around

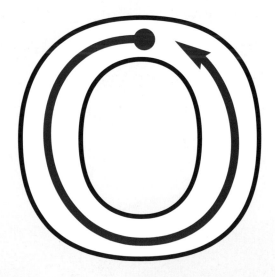

Some words to familiarise:

cow hen duck

High-frequency words:

we   the   go   are   up

Tips for Reading 'Go Away!'

- *Practise the words listed above before reading the story.*

- *If the reader struggles with any of the other words, ask them to look for sounds they know in the word. Encourage them to sound out the words and help them read the words if necessary.*

- *After reading the story, ask the reader whether they know why the animals were hungry.*

Fun Activity

Do you have any pets to feed?

How long do you like to stay in bed for?

Go Away!

The cows say "Moo! Moo!"
"We are hungry."

The dogs go "Ruff! Ruff!"
"We are hungry."

The hens say "Cluck! Cluck!"
"We are hungry."

The ducks go "Quack! Quack!"
"We are hungry."

"Moo! Moo! Ruff! Ruff!
Cluck! Cluck! Quack! Quack!"

"We are hungry."

The farmer's mum yells "Get up!"

The Letter L

Trace the lower and upper case letter with a finger. Sound out the letter.

Down

Down,
cross

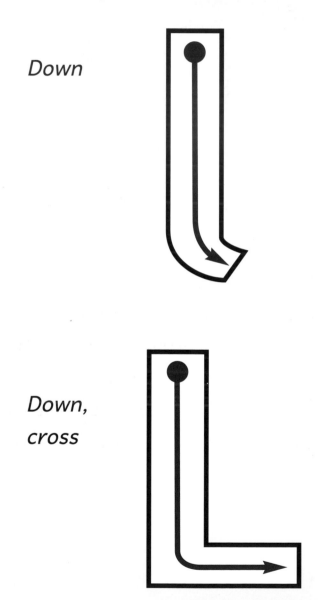

Some words to familiarise:

ship truck rocket

High-frequency words:

I a in we it no are all go

Tips for Reading 'Let's Make a Rocket'

- Practise the words listed above before reading the story.

- If the reader struggles with any of the other words, ask them to look for sounds they know in the word. Encourage them to sound out the words and help them read the words if necessary.

- After reading the story, ask the reader if they remember the first thing that was made.

Fun Activity

Have a go at building your own rocket!

Let's Make a Rocket

"I will make a den," said Pip.

"I can sit in it."

Dens are fun!

"I will make a ship," said Fizz.

"I can sail in it."

Ships are fun!

"I will make a car," said Biff.

"I will make a truck," said Mop.

"I can ride in it."

"We can make a big rocket.
We can all go in it."

They all make a rocket.

They all go in it.

Book Bands for Guided Reading

Dog in a Dress and Run, Tom, Run!	Buzz and Jump! Jump!	Bam-Boo and I Wish	Sam the Star and Clown Fun!	Seeds and Stuck in the Tree
978-1-84886-290-6	978-1-84886-250-0	978-1-84886-251-7	978-1-84886-288-3	978-1-84886-289-0
Viv the Vet and Top Dog	Go Away! and Let's Make A Rocket	Catch It, Jess! and Cat Nap	Grandad's Cake and Grandad's Pot	Zoom! and Come Back, Mack!
978-1-84886-347-7	978-1-84886-350-7	978-1-84886-348-4	978-1-84886-351-4	978-1-84886-349-1

Plus many more titles in the scheme!

To view the whole Maverick Readers scheme, please visit:

www.maverickbooks.co.uk/early-readers

The Institute of Education book banding system is a scale of colours that reflects the various levels of reading difficulty. The bands are assigned by taking into account the content, the language style, the layout and phonics.

Maverick Early Readers are a bright, attractive range of books covering the pink to purple bands. All of these books have been book banded for guided reading to the industry standard and edited by a leading educational consultant.